TRY NOT TO
CHALLENGE
Joke Book
TEEN
Edition
Teenager Jokes & Tricky Riddles!
D0833503

HOWLING
MOON BOOKS

© 2019 Howling Moon Books

© 2019 Illustrations by Salem Dcat

ALL RIGHTS RESERVED. This Book or parts thereof may not be reproduced in any form, stored in any retrieval system, or transmitted by any means electronic, mechanical, photocopy, recording, or otherwise without prior written permission of the publisher, Howling Moon Books or Author, C.S. Adams, Illustrator Salem Dcat, except as provided by United States of America Copyright Law.

14
LOL
13
16
LOL
17
18
15
13
19
LOL

# Try Not to Laugh Challenge™ Teen Edition

## Rules:

Put on your STRAIGHT FACE & your THINKING CAP!

Pick your team, or go one on one.

Take turns reading the Jokes and Riddles to each other.

Start with reading a Joke or a Tricky Riddle in the funniest way possible. You can make silly faces, hilarious sound effects, goofy voices, wacky movements or anything laughable!

## Jokes:

If your opponent laughs or cracks a smile, you get a point!

## Tricky Riddles:

If your opponent cannot answer the Riddle, you get 1 point! Bonus...If you can make them laugh when you are reading the Riddle or when they are guessing the answer, you get an additional point!

## Your Goal?

Win as many points as possible! First team to win 10 points, or the most points, **Wins!**

Note:

You can make the game short with a total of 10 points, or longer with a total of 30 points, or more. You can split the book up and play in rounds, or go through the whole book until you reach the end if you want...it is up to you!

# JOKES

What do teens despise the most?

When teachers tell the class that something isn't going to be on the test, and IT IS!

When do teens secretly cry inside?

When teachers load them up with homework on the weekend!

How much do teenagers enjoy doing their laundry?

Loads!

Why are teenagers always hungry?

They are too busy posting photos of their meals!

How do you get a teen to talk to you?

Hide the game controller!

What do dogs do after they finish obedience school?

They get their masters!

Why did the gamer cut his walk outside short?

Because the graphics weren't that great!

What happens when you make your friends leave a concert early?

You will never hear the end of it!

Which two months are hard to trust?

FIBruary and JuLIE!

What do spies do in the rain?

They go undercover!

What happened when the teen CONDUCTED SHOCKINGLY bad behavior?

He was GROUNDED!

What did the cellphone say to the landline?

Hi Grandma!

What is Tayler Swift's favorite kind of makeup?

SHADE!

What security computer question do droids dislike?

Are you a robot?

When do computers get new shoes?

When they REBOOT!

What do you call a trip to Starbucks?

A Grande Adventure!

What are braces for?

A place to store leftover food!

What does Santa keep in his computer?

Cookies!

What is Baby Yoda's motto?

Do or Not Do, there is No Cry!

Why did Jack and Jill go up the hill?

To get better Wi-Fi!

Why did the Star Wars movies come out in the order of
4 5 6 1 2 3 7 8 9?

In charge of the sequence, Yoda was!

Why is it hard to believe a goat?

Because they are always KIDDING!

Why don't teenagers talk to circles?

There is no point!

Why aren't gamers quitters?

Because they don't need to quit, they can just RESTART!

What kind of pants do all teenagers wear?

Smarty pants!

What kind of dog is found in packs?

Hot dogs!

Why do tweens play Minecraft?

Because they are MINORS!

Why aren't teens good at math?

Because they can't even!

Why was the doorknob mad?

It didn't get its turn!

What is it called when you are on the perimeter of your WiFi range?

Router Limits!

# TRICKY RIDDLES

You arrive to enter, but you may not come in, I have space, but no room, I have lots of keys that open no lock. What is it?

A computer!

What do you have to break before you use it?

An egg!

If two's company, three's a crowd, what is 4 and 5?

Nine!

What gets sharper the more you use it!

Your brain!

What has no beginning, end, or middle?

A doughnut!

Drop me and I am sure to crack.
Look at me and I will smile back.
What am I?

A mirror!

There were six birds in a bird bath.
A hawk swoops in and takes 1.
How many birds are left now?

None. All the birds got scared and flew away!

What comes once in a second, twice in a season, but never at the end of the year?

The letter S!

What is easy to get into, but hard to get out of?

Trouble!

The dirtier I am, the whiter I get. What am I?

A chalkboard!

What four days start with T?

Tuesday, Thursday, Today and Tomorrow!

I'm tall when I'm young, and
I'm short when I'm old.
What am I?

A candle!

What two letters are very jealous?

NV!

How many times can you take 1 away from 5?

Only once, the next time you will be taking 1 from 4!

When you are trying to find something, why is it always in the LAST place you look?

Because when you find it, you stop looking!

What language do all people speak without saying a word?

Body language!

What kind of band doesn't play music?

An hair band!

# JOKES

How do you get a teen to show up for dinner?

Change the WiFi password!

Why shouldn't teens drink too much coffee?

It can cause a LATTE problems!

What is a taco's favorite lullabye?

Soft taco, warm taco, little
ball of meat, happy taco,
sleepy taco, eat, eat, eat!

What do you wear when you muck out a horse stall?

DUNG-arees!

How do you say good-bye to steak sauce?

Have A1-derful day!

Why do teens like prefixes?

Because they put the PRO into PROCRASTINATION!

Why did Yoda turn Santa's sleigh around?

Because he always reverses clauses!

How did the teen feel when her favorite shoes fell apart?

She was SOLE bummed out!

What eight-character password does Walt Disney use?

Snow White and the Seven Dwarfs!

What do you call a wizard with airbuds?

Airy-Podder!

Why were the Middle Ages called the Dark Ages?

Because there were lots of KNIGHTS!

Why did the candles go out?

Because they liked each other!

What is another name for coffee?

Survival Juice!

What does a pimple do when you are sleeping?

It just ZITS there!

What do you call a ditsy bird?

A featherbrain!

What cab company works out at the gym?

LIFT!

Where does the earth keep its photos?

In the clouds!

Why was the teen hearing voices in her head?

She was wearing her earbuds!

What can mess up your Friday?

Realizing that it is only Wednesday!

What happens when a cow laughs too hard?

Milk comes out of her nose!

What is a teen's definition of infinity?

Tonight's homework!

What knight was not good at chess?

Sir Render!

Why don't programmers like nature?

It has too many bugs!

Teens know that education is important.

But, Video Games are more importanter!

When are teens like a snake?

When they are rattled!

When is it a good time at night to change Baby Yoda's diaper?

In the wee wee hours!

What is the best thing to have in the school cafeteria?

A fire drill!

Where is the best place in New York City to do your math homework?

Times Square!

Teenagers are really good at falling asleep.

They can do it with their eyes closed!

What kind of make-up do ghosts wear?

Mas-SCARE-a!

How much sleep do teens need?

Just 5 more minutes!

# TRICKY RIDDLES

What is put on the table and cut, but never eaten?

A deck of cards!

What kind of sides does a circle have?

Two, the inside and the outside!

What runs around on its head all day?

A nail in a horseshoe!

What is harder to catch, the faster you run?

Your breath!

At what temperature does boiling water boil?

The temperature that it is at, it is already boiling!

What is as big as a dinosaur but doesn't weigh anything?

Its shadow!

How do you kick a soccer ball 5 feet and it returns to you?

You kick it straight up!

I am everything if you turn
me on my side,
But if you cut me in half,
I am nothing,
Kind of like I died.
What am I?

8!

What is the most curious letter?

Y!

What can go through a door, but
never goes in or out of the room?

A keyhole!

I can be used to greet you or say goodbye.
I can be planted, but not in the ground.
I can be sent without a sound.
What am I?

A Kiss!

What time is spelled the same backward and forward?

Noon!

What question can you ask all day long;
Yet get different answers, none of them wrong?

"What time is it?"

The teenager wins a race in his flip-flops. What place did he get if he is racing against 2 track stars?

First Place, since he did win the race!

# JOKES

What do you call a teen's pile of laundry?

Mount Wash More!

What is an avocado's favorite music?

Guac n' Roll!

Why did the zombie fail his driving test?

He left his foot on the gas!

What is red, brown, white and tastes like cardboard?

High School cafeteria pizza!

Why isn't UBER popular?

Because they drive people away!

What do you call a bunch of bad teens?

A weapon of MASS DYSFUNCTION!

Which teens live dangerously?

The ones who do their math homework in PEN!

Why were the cellphones worried about the landline?

It never leaves the house!

Why do teens take so many selfies?

They have no selfie control!

Some teens don't enjoy playing soccer.

They do it just for kicks!

When do teens panic?

When their phone battery is at 1%!

What did the caveman order at the cafeteria?

A club sandwich!

Why do teens want king-sized beds?

They want to DREAM BIG!

What do you call a pre-teen comedian?

A KIDDER!

Why didn't the nut like checkers?

It was a CHESS-nut!

What social media does a musician use?

Rap-chat!

Why are chemistry jokes kind of boring?

Because they lack the ELEMENT of surprise!

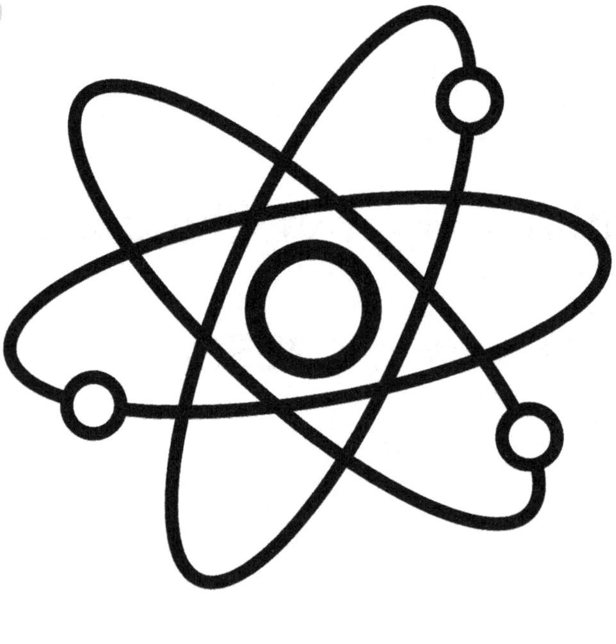

Why does tomato soup and chicken noodle soup have in common?

They are BROTH-ers!

Why couldn't anyone play the teen's video game?

Because she was a controller freak!

What do you call a turkey in the winter?

A Brrrrr-d!

# TRICKY RIDDLES

Up and down I go,
Yet I do not move;
I can be a place to sit,
And a place to stay fit.
What am I?

A flight of stairs!

I have no eyes, no ears or legs,
yet I am able to move the earth;
Gardeners think my poop has worth.
What am I?

An earthworm!

I sing, I make sounds to anyone around;
I insist on an answer,
Yet no question will be found.
What am I?

A cellphone!

When I am up, all is bright;
When I am down, it will feel like night;
A toddler cannot reach me at this height.
What am I?

A light switch!

I fly without wings, I cry without eyes,
I can be light or dark.
What am I?

A cloud!

A rancher has sixty-seven llamas. All but nine of them run away. How many llamas does he have left?

Nine.

I can breathe the air without a mouth;
I will hurt anyone who comes too near;
I dance to music I cannot hear.
What am I?

Fire!

My legs go up and my legs
go down;
Sometimes I go fast;
Sometimes I go slow;
Yet nowhere do I go.
What am I?

An Elliptical!

I can give you hours of enjoyment;
but I can also make you crazy mad;
Yet if someone takes me from you,
you will be quite sad.
What am I?

A video game!

What does Frosty the Snowman and Perry the Platypus have in common?

Their middle name, the.

I am always in front of you;
Unseen, yet quite close;
Once I am here, I am gone;
Where? ...nobody knows.
What am I?

Tomorrow!

What looks like poo, but doesn't stink;
You can add it to your writings, but it isn't ink.

A poop emoji!

What is brown and sticky?

A tree!

In what year did Christmas and New Year's Day land in the same year?

Every year!

I have six faces;
but I cannot grin;
I have twenty-one eyes;
but I don't have a chin.
What am I?

A DIE (DICE)

# JOKES

What do hobbits bring on camping trips?

Sleeping BAGGINS!

How did the teens like the party punch?

It was a HIT!

Why can't neutrons use a credit card?

They have no charge!

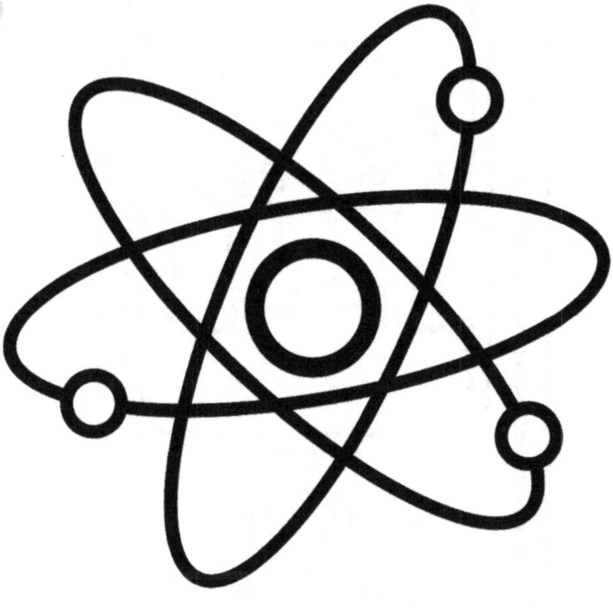

What class has the most makeup exams?

Cosmetology class!

Why are teens so fearless?

Even when they have an awful selfie, they post it anyway!

Why does anyone still want a landline?

To call their cellphone when it is missing!

What is better than summer vacation?

More summer vacation!

What do you call 288 cafeteria lunches?

Two Gross!
(1 gross = 144 things)

Why should you use earbuds wires for your shoelaces?

Because they would tie themselves!

Who is famous for his prank calls, has yellow spikey hair, is very smelly?

Fart Simpson!

Why did the bridge go to the doctor?

Something came over him!

Why couldn't the gel pen cross the road?

It was stationary!

What do you call a skunk who can see the future?

A fortune SMELLER!

How do you park a computer?

You back it up!

Why don't astronauts pack their skateboards for a trip into space?

Because they can't get AIR there!

What kind of haircut do bees get?

Buzzz-cuts!

What really makes teenagers mad?

When their selfie is photobombed!

How do trees find their ancestors?

They trace their ROOTS!

Why do ghosts go to concerts?

They have the best SHEETS in the house!

What is the most musical vegetable?

BEET-hoven!

What train is the smartest?

The train of thought!

What do you call headphones that can't keep a charge?

Deadbeats!

What month do teens sleep the least?

February, it is the shortest month of the year!

Why didn't the teen tell the joke about the bad bargain?

It wasn't WORTH it!

How does the swim team get to their meet?

In a carpool!

Why didn't the teen get around to starting her homework?

She was too busy posting reasons why she didn't want to do it!

Why don't you want lightning on your bowling team?

Because lightning never strikes twice!

Why is 13 an unlucky number for Dad and Mom?

They now have an Official Teenager!

How did the ballerina get the lead role in the play?

She was on her toes!

What's the difference between the ACT and SAT?

One letter!

Why aren't there knock-knock jokes about freedom?

Because freedom rings!

Why was the cloud upset?

Someone stole his thunder!

Why did the selfie go to prison?

It was framed!

If you could put cafeteria food in one category, what would that be?

Mystery food!

Why didn't the oil want to hang out with the water?

He was a hydro-phobe!

Our school lunch is so bad!

Most kids say grace before, during and after the meal!

## Available from Howling Moon Books

# Available from Howling Moon Books

Available from Howling Moon Books

# Available from Howling Moon Books

14
16
13
HA
HA
HA
17
HA
HA
HA
19
15
18

# Teen Edition

Congratulations!
You have survived an umpteen amount of Crazy Teen Jokes & Tricky Riddles!

Please consider leaving us a review on Amazon.com. We value your feedback & greatly appreciate your time!

Thank you
Howling Moon Books

Made in the USA
Middletown, DE
01 October 2020

20852575R00046